70 YEARS OF POPULAR MUSIC

THE NINETIES

PART ONE

Production: STEPHEN CLARK and SADIE COOK

Published 1994

IMP

© International Music Publications Limited
Southend Road, Woodford Green, Essex IG8 8HN, England.

ALL WOMAN

Words and Music by STANSFIELD, DEVANEY and MORRIS

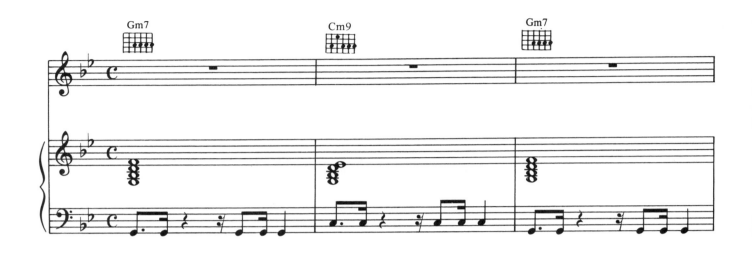

(1.) He's home a-gain_ from an -oth-er day, she
(Verses 2 & 3, see at bottom)

smiles at him as he walks through the door._ She won-ders if it will

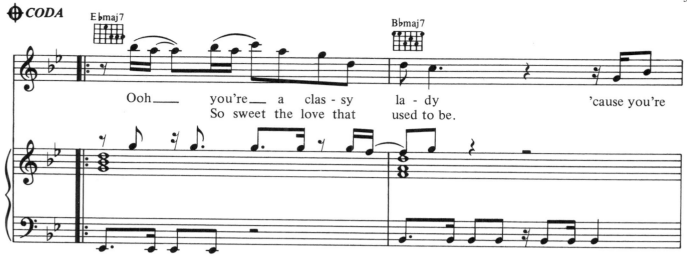

VERSE 2:
She stands there and lets the tears flow
Tears that she's been holding back so long
She wonders where did all the loving go
The love they used to share when they were strong.

She says yes, I look a mess
But I don't love you any less
I thought you always thought enough of me
To always be impressed.

CHORUS 2:
I may not be a lady
But I'm all woman
From Monday to Sunday I work my fingers to the bone
I'm no classy lady
But I'm all woman
This woman needs a little love to make her strong
You're not the only one.

VERSE 3:
He holds her and hangs his head in shame
He doesn't see her like he used to do
He's too wrapped up in working for his pay
He hasn't seen the pain he's put her through.

Attention that he paid
Just vanished in the haze
He remembers how it used to be
When he used to say.

CHORUS 3:
You'll always be a lady
'Cause you're all woman
From Monday to Sunday I love you much more than you know
You're a classy lady
'Cause you're all woman
This woman needs a loving man to keep her warm.

ARE YOU GONNA GO MY WAY?

Words and Music by LENNY KRAVITZ and CRAIG ROSS

9

Are you gonna go my

way?

'Cos ba - by I got to know.

VERSE 2:

I don't know why we always cry,
This we must leave and get undone.
We must engage and rearrange
And turn this planet back to one.
So tell me why we got to die
And kill each other one by one.
We've got to hug and rub-a-dub,
We've got to dance and be in love.
But what I really want to know is
Are you gonna go my way?
And I got to, got to know.

BE MY BABY

Words by LENNY KRAVITZ and GERRY DEVEAUZ
Music by LENNY KRAVITZ

(1.) I saw you walk down the street ___ with some ___ oth - er girl, ___ yeah,

al - ways thought that I was ___ the on - ly one in your world ___

12

14

I want you to love____ me ba - by.

Repeat to Fade

VERSE 2:
Love is just like a flower, baby it has to grow, yeah.
And when you are away I'm even loving you more.
I just have to let you know
One on one is the way and that's the way it should be, yeah.
So if you're not gonna stay then don't be playing with me,
You can set me free.

CHORUS 2:
All I'm asking you for when you walk out the door
Is to be my baby, baby
'Cause all this love is for you and you know that I'm true
And I'll be your baby.
Continue to additional chorus

(D.S.) VERSE 3:
I remember our walk the other Saturday night,
Sweet harmonies filled and floated through our minds.
Never felt this way before.
We were riding so high on love and understanding,
So why go wasting your time when you have got such a find
That is everlasting?

CHORUS 3: — *As Chorus 1*[O]

ADDITIONAL CHORUS:
All I'm asking you for when you walk out the door
Is to be my baby, baby
'Cause all this love is for you and you know that I'm true,
And I'll be your baby.
To Coda

DAMN, I WISH I WAS YOUR LOVER

Words and Music by SOPHIE B HAWKINS

DON'T LET THE SUN GO DOWN ON ME

Words and Music by ELTON JOHN and BERNIE TAUPIN

DRIVEN BY YOU

Words and Music by BRIAN MAY

Verse 2: Well it's tough to make a journey through
The right stuff is dead ahead of you and me
And you know we've still got time.

Hold on tight to the driving wheel
And this ride is really out of line
Raw deal, but there's no other that's worth a dime

You know I love you but you drive me crazy
'Cause you're saying all the things I want to say to you
Everything I do is driven by you.

D.S. Now we're never gonna know who's dreaming
But we're working night and day to make a dream come true
Everything I do is driven by you.

END OF THE ROAD

Words and Music by BABYFACE, L A REID and DARYL SIMMONS

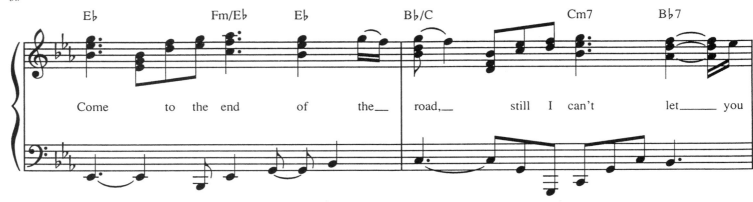

Verse 2:
Girl, I know you really love me, you just don't realize.
You've never been there before, it's only your first time.
Maybe I'll forgive you, mmm. . . maybe you'll try.
We should be happy together, forever, you and I.

Bridge 2:
Could you love me again like you loved me before?
This time, I want you to love me much more.
This time, instead just come back to my bed.
And baby, just don't let me down.

Verse 3, spoken:
Girl I'm here for you.
All those times at night when you just hurt me,
And just ran out with that other fellow,
Baby, I knew about it.
I just didn't care.
You just don't understand how much I love you, do you?
I'm here for you.
I'm not out to go out there and cheat all night just like you did, baby.
But that's alright, huh, I love you anyway.
And I'm still gonna be here for you 'til my dyin' day, baby.
Right now, I'm just in so much pain, baby,
'Cause you just won't come back to me, will you?
Just come back to me.

Bridge 3, spoken:
Yes, baby, my heart is lonely.
My heart hurts, baby, yes, I feel pain too.
Baby please . . .

GET HERE

Words and Music by BRENDA RUSSELL

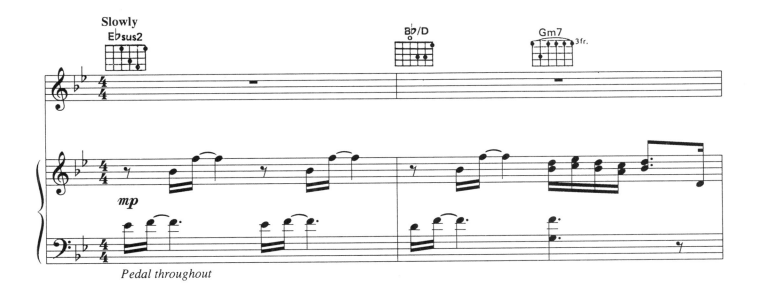

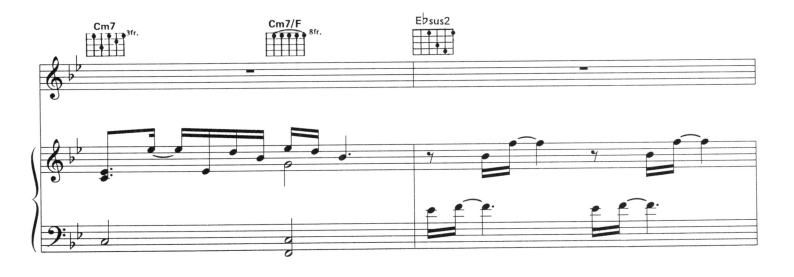

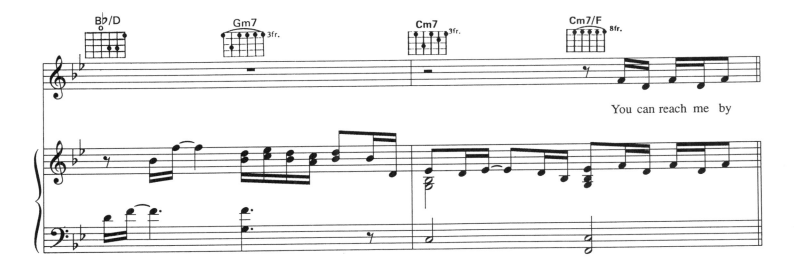

You can reach me by

I don't care how you get here, just get here if _____ you can. _____

Tacet

ritard.

GIVE IN TO ME

Written and Composed by MICHAEL JACKSON and BILL BOTTRELL

HOLDING ON

Words and Music by BEVERLEY CRAVEN

I DROVE ALL NIGHT

Words and Music by BILLY STEINBERG and TOM KELLY

53

54

56

HEAL THE WORLD

Written and Composed by MICHAEL JACKSON
Prelude by MARTY PAICH

62

63

I'D DO ANYTHING FOR LOVE (BUT I WON'T DO THAT)

Words and Music by JIM STEINMAN

Lyrics:

No, I won't do ___ that.

Some days it don't ___ come eas - y,
Some nights you're breath - ing fire,
Some days I pray ___ for si - lence,

some days it don't ___ come hard. ___
some nights you're carved ___ in ice. ___
some days I pray ___ for soul. ___

I'LL BE THERE

Words and Music by BERRY GORDY, HAL DAVIES,
WILLIE HUTCH and BOB WEST

2. I'll reach out my hand to you:
   I'll have faith in all you do.
   Just call my name and I'll be there.

3. Let me fill your heart with joy and laughter.
   Togetherness, girl, is all I'm after:
   Whenever you need me, I'll be there.
   I'll be there to protect you,
   With unselfish love that respects you.
   Just call my name, I'll be there.

IT'S MY LIFE

Words and Music by DR ALBAN and DENNIZ POP

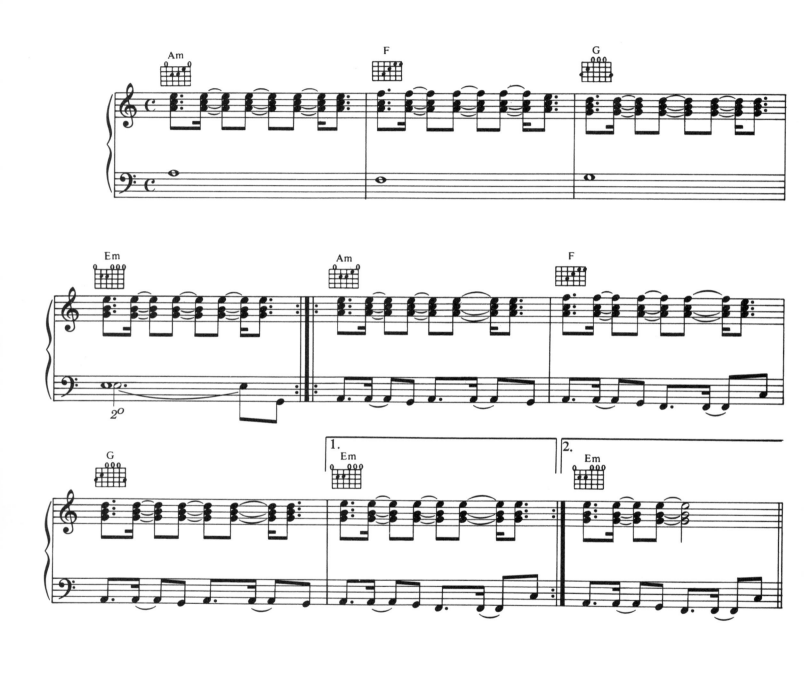

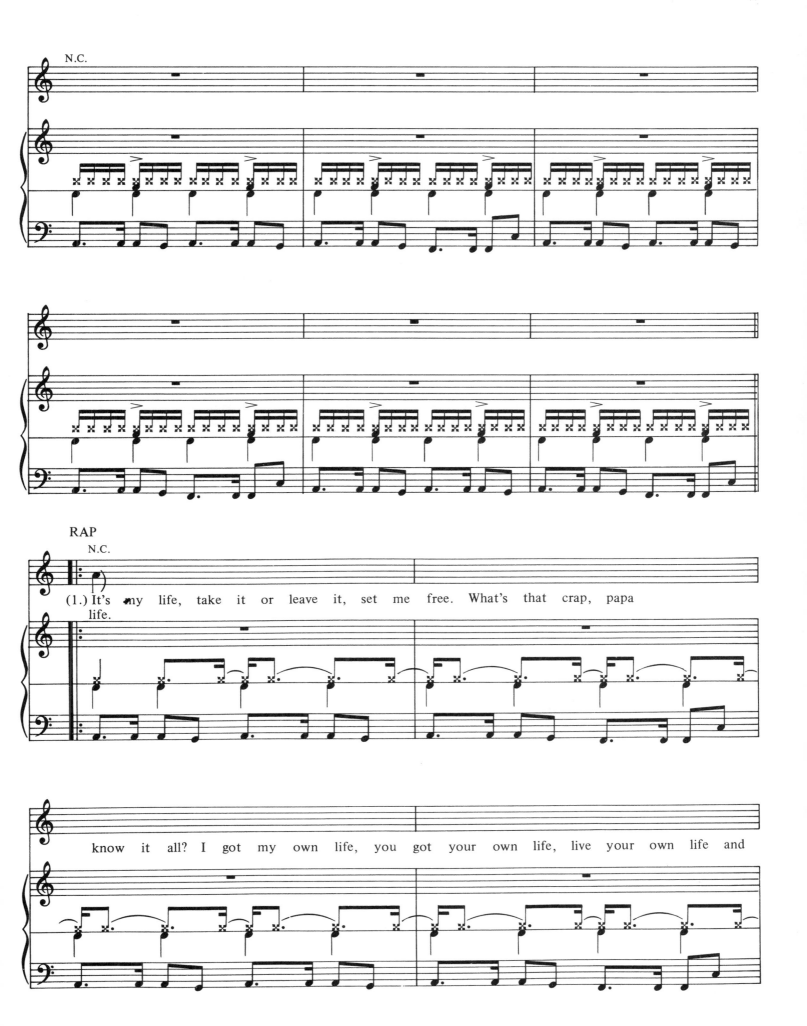

RAP

(1.) It's my life, take it or leave it, set me free. What's that crap, papa
life.

know it all? I got my own life, you got your own life, live your own life and

78

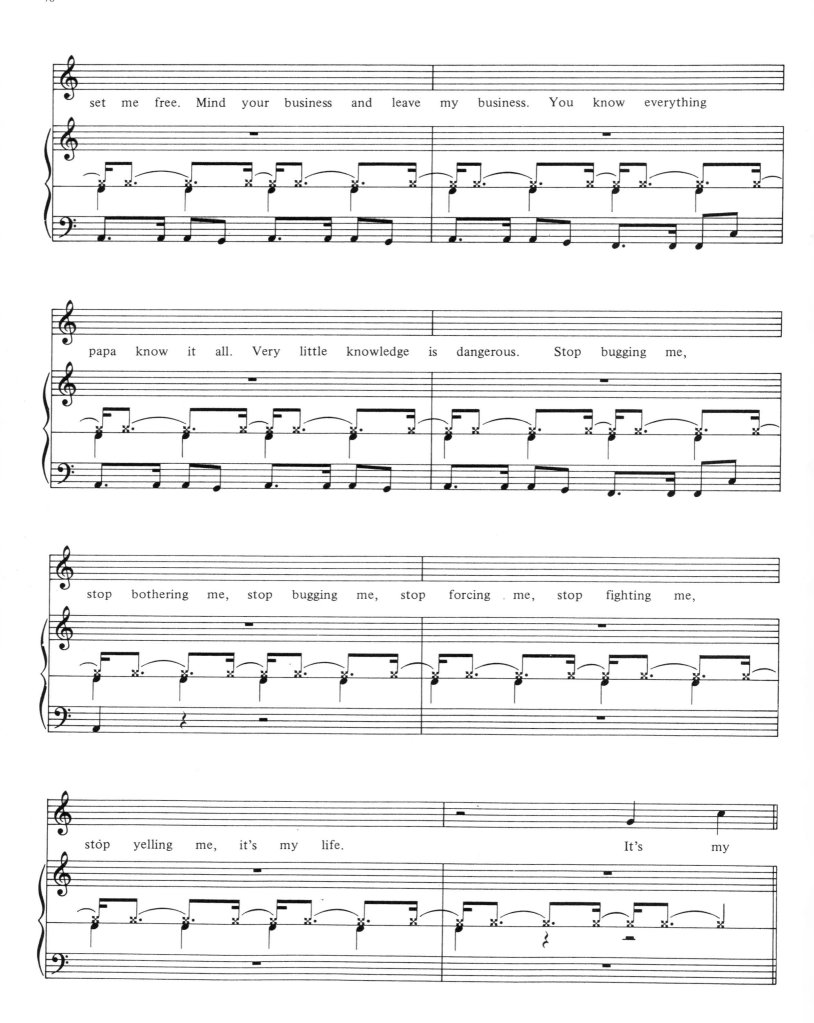

80

RAP 2:
Do you understand? I live the way I want to live,
I make decisions day and night, show me signs and good examples.
Stop telling people how to run your business, take a trip to East and West.
You find that you don't know anything, every's getting tired of you.
Sometimes you have to look and listen, you can even learn from me.
Little knowledge is dangerous, it's my life.

RAP 3:
Set me free, so you bad so you lie
What you see is what you get, listen to people and sort things out.
Things I do I do them no more, things I say I say them no more.
Changes comes once in life; stop hugging me, stop bothering me,
Stop bugging me, stop forcing me, stop fighting me, stop yelling me,
Stop telling me, stop seeing me, it's my life.

I WILL ALWAYS LOVE YOU

Words and Music by DOLLY PARTON

82

83

Verse 3: Instrumental solo

Verse 4:
I hope life treats you kind
And I hope you have all you've dreamed of.
And I wish to you, joy and happiness.
But above all this, I wish you love.
(To Chorus:)

THE JOKER

Words and Music by A ERTEGUN, EDDIE CURTIS and STEVE MILLER

88

2. You're the cutest thing that I ever did see;
   I really love your peaches, want to shake your tree.
   Lovey dovey, lovey dovey, lovey dovey all the time;
   Come on baby I'll show you a real good time.

JUST ANOTHER DAY

Words and Music by JON SECADA and MIGUEL A MOREJON

Verse 2:
Making the time,
Find the right lines to make you stay forever.
What do I have to tell you?
Just trying to hold on to something.
    (Trying to hold on to something good.)
Give us a chance to make it.
    (Give us a chance to make it.)

Bridge 2:
Don't wanna hold on to never . . .
I'm not that strong, I'm not that strong.
(To Chorus:)

Bridge 3:
Why can't you stay forever?
Just give me a reason, give me a reason.
(To Chorus:)

JUSTIFIED & ANCIENT

Words and Music by JAMES CAUTY, BILL DRUMMOND and RICKY LYTE

All _____ bound for mu mu land, _____ all _____ bound for mu mu land, _____ hey. Hey hey, _____ all _____ bound for mu mu land. _____ mu mu land. _____ They're

98

VERSE 2:
They're justified and they're ancient
And they drive an ice cream van,
    (Just roll it from the top)
They're justified and they're ancient
With still no master plan
    (To the bridge, to the bridge, to the bridge now).

The last train left an hour ago
They were singing all aboard
All bound for mu mu land
The someone started screaming, turn up the strobe!

RAP:
Justified and ancient, ancient and justified
Rockin' to the rhythm in the ice cream van
With the plan and the key to enter into mu mu
Vibes from the jibes of the jams
I know where the P.D.'s at 'cause I know what time it is
Threes on the dial, make mine a 99
New style, meanwhile lost on a mission
While fishing in the rivers of life.

NOVEMBER RAIN

Words and Music by W AXL ROSE, SLASH,
DUFF McKAGAN and IZZY STRADLIN'

* Recorded a half step lower

ken heart,___ would- n't time___ be out___ to charm___ you? Woh.___

A MILLION LOVE SONGS

Words and Music by GARY BARLOW

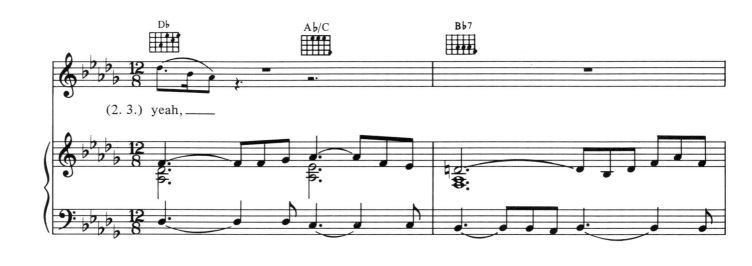

113

VERSE 2:
Looking to the future now, this is what I see,
A million chances pass me by, a million chances to hold you.
Take me back, take me back to where I used to be,
Hide away from all my truths, through the light I see.

CHORUS:
A million love songs later,
Here I am trying to tell you that I care.
A million love songs later,
And here I am, just for you girl;
A million love songs later,
Here I am.

THE ONE AND ONLY

Words and Music by NIK KERSHAW

116

you are the one___ and on - ly, you.___

D.S. Repeat Chorus

CODA

PROMISE ME

Words and Music by BEVERLEY CRAVEN

121

And I'll be home, I'll be home soon.

I'll be home

soon.

RHYTHM IS A DANCER

Words and Music by BENITO BENITES,
JOHN GARRETT III and THEA AUSTIN

RAP:

Let the rhythm ride you, guide you,   sneak inside you, set your mind to move to its pulsation.
When, let it control you   hold you. mould you, not the old,   the new, touch it taste it

Bass vibration, synth sensation   pause, it's not in place   In mind and body must be free to
Free your soul when let it base you   Got to be what you wanna   if the groove don't get you the rhyme flow's

SALTWATER

Words and Music by JULIAN LENNON, LESLIE SPIRO and MARK SPIRO

Verse 2:.
We climb the highest mountain
we'll make the desert bloom
We're so ingenious
We can walk on the moon
But when I hear of how
The forests have died
Saltwater wells in my eyes.

Verse 3:
We light the desert ocean
Send photographs of Mars
We're so enchanted by
How clever we are
Why should one baby
Feel so hungry she cries
Saltwater wells in my eyes.

Verse 4:
We are a rock revolving
Around a golden sun
We are a billion children
Rolled into one
What will I think of me
The day that I die
Saltwater wells in my eyes.

SACRIFICE

Words and Music by ELTON JOHN and BERNIE TAUPIN

134

THE SHOOP SHOOP SONG (IT'S IN HIS KISS)

Words and Music by RUDY CLARK

SHOW ME HEAVEN

Words and Music by JAY RIFKIN, ERIC RACKIN and MARIA McKEE

139

SLEEPING SATELLITE

Words and Music by TASMIN ARCHER,
JOHN BECK and JOHN HUGHES

Don't blame this sleep-ing sa-tel-lite.

(1.) Did we
(2. *See lyric at bottom*)

fly to the moon too soon, did we squan-der the chance in the rush of the

race, the rea-son we chase is lost in ro-mance._ And still we

try_____ to jus-ti-fy the waste for a taste of man's great-est_ ad-ven-ture oh._

VERSE 2:

Have we got what it takes to advance?
Have we peaked too soon?
If the world is so green
Then why does it scream under a blue moon?
We wonder why
If the earth's sacrificed
For the price of its greatest treasure.

VERSE 3 (D.S.)

And when we shoot for the stars
What a giant step;
Have we got what it takes
To carry the weight of this concept
Or pass it by?
Like a shot in the dark
Miss the mark with a sense of adventure.

SMELLS LIKE TEEN SPIRIT

Words and Music by KURT COBAIN,
CHRIS NOVOSELIC and DAVID GROHL

Load up____ on guns,____ bring____ your friends.
I'm worse at what I____ do best____
And I____ for - get____ just why____ I taste.

149

SOMEDAY (I'M COMING BACK)

Words and Music by STANSFIELD, DEVANEY and MORRIS

Some-day I'm com-ing back

and it won't be long, be-fore you call me and

tell me to come home.

152

153

VERSE 2:
Even in stormy weather, we always stuck together.
You always kept me near, were so sincere.
So why so sudden the change of heart
Why do I feel like I've done wrong?
When all that I want is that you ask me to come back home.

VERSE 3:
(8 bars instrumental)
So why so sudden the change of heart
Why do I feel like I've done wrong?
When all that I want is that you ask me to come back home.

STAY

Words by SIOBHAN FAHEY and DAVID A STEWART
Music by SIOBHAN FAHEY, MARCY LEVY and DAVID A STEWART

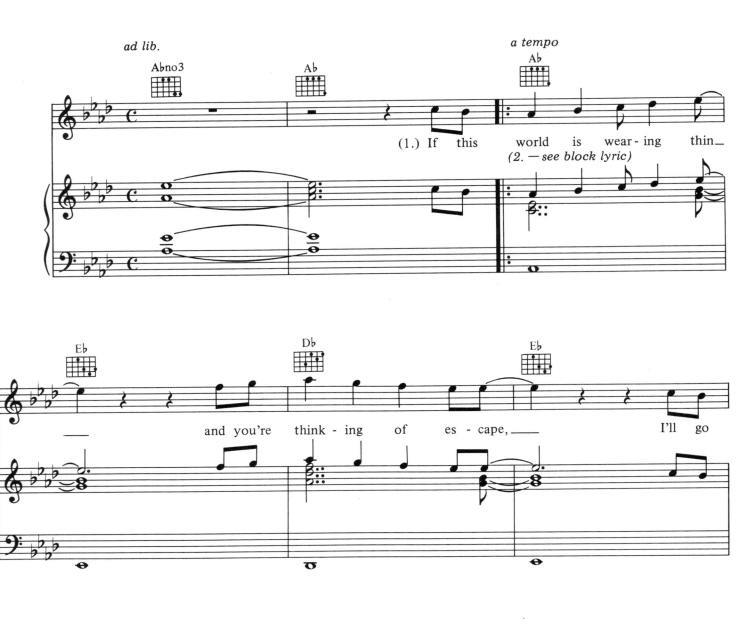

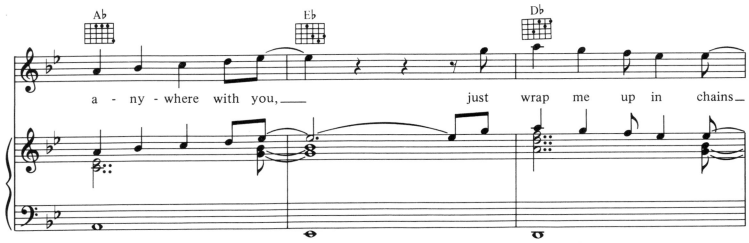

own— world, on - ly time will tell— if you can

break the spell— back in your own— world.

D.S. Repeat
Chorus to Fade

VERSE 2:
In the silence of your room,
In the darkness of your dreams,
You must only think of me,
There can be no in between.
When your pride is on the floor,
I'll make you beg for more.

THESE ARE THE DAYS OF OUR LIVES

Words and Music by QUEEN

© 1991 Queen Music Ltd, UK
EMI Music Publishing Ltd, London WC2H 0EA

When life's just a game,___ no use in sit-tin' and a-think-

-in' on what you did,___ when you can sit back___ and en-joy it through your kids.

Some-times it seems like late-ly I just don't know, bet-ter sit back

and go___ with the flow.___ (Cos)

164

Those were the days of our lives, yeah, the

TOO FUNKY

Words and Music by GEORGE MICHAEL

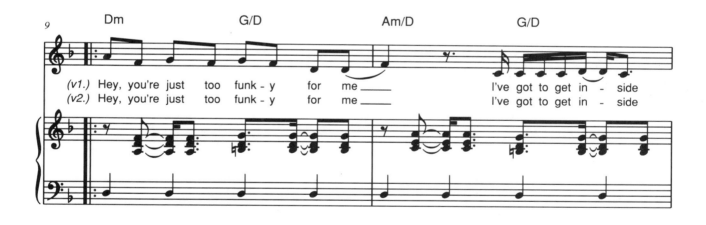

(v1.) Hey, you're just too funk - y for me ____ I've got to get in - side
(v2.) Hey, you're just too funk - y for me ____ I've got to get in - side

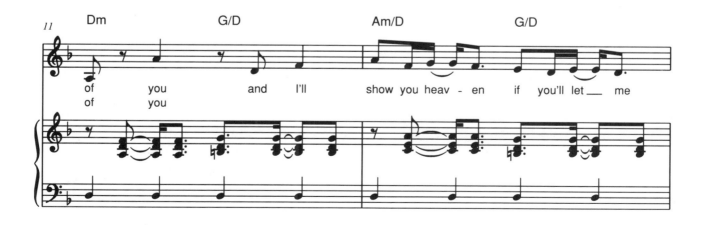

of you and I'll show you heav - en if you'll let ___ me
of you

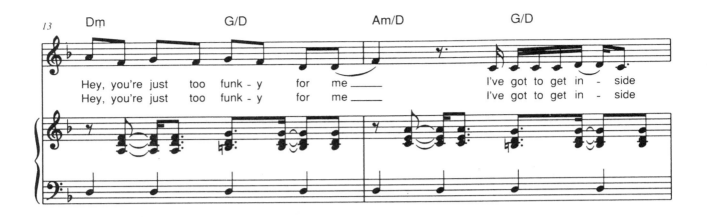

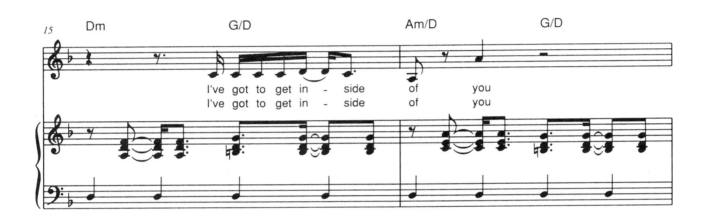

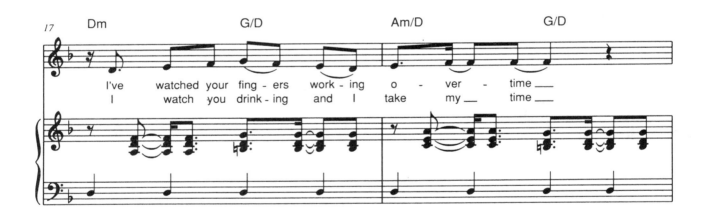

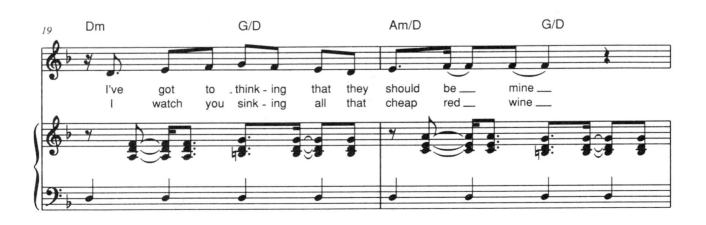

I'd love to see you na-ked ba-by I'd like to think that some-time may-
I've got to see you na-ked ba-by I'd like to think that some-time may-

- be to-night   if   that's al - right
- be to-night   my   goal's in   sight

(solo keyboard)

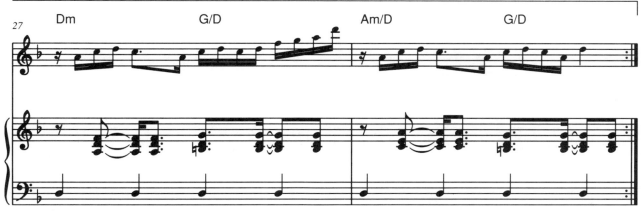

170

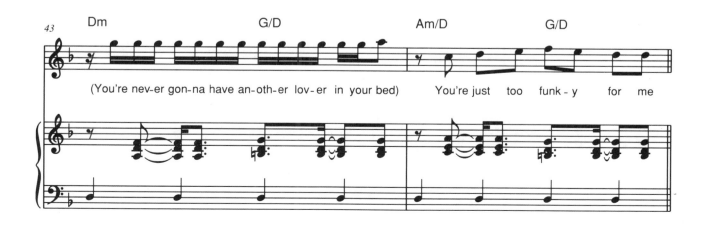

172

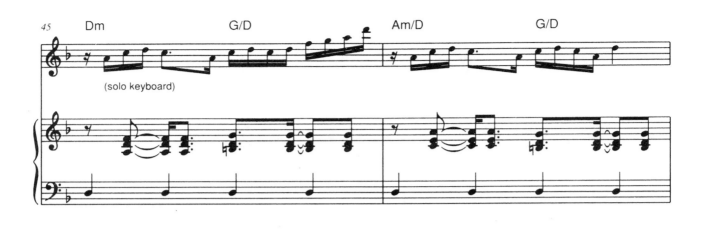

(solo keyboard)

(Would you

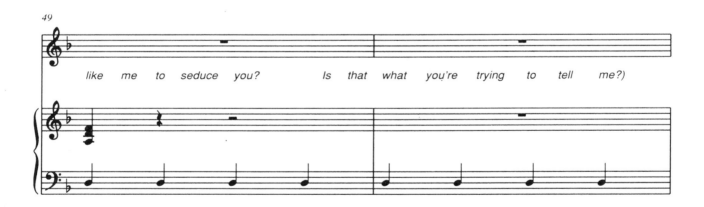

like me to seduce you? Is that what you're trying to tell me?)

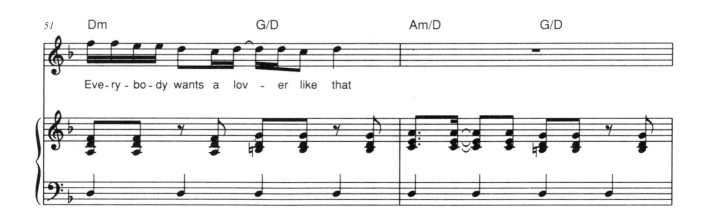

Eve-ry-bo-dy wants a lov - er like that

174

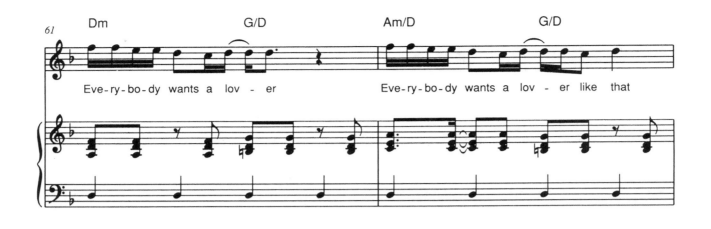

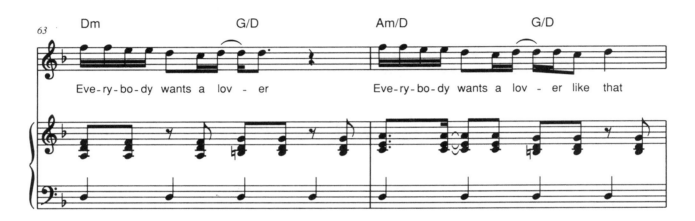

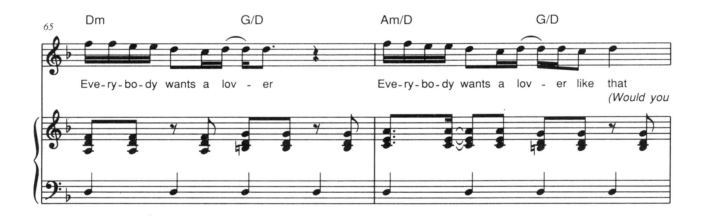

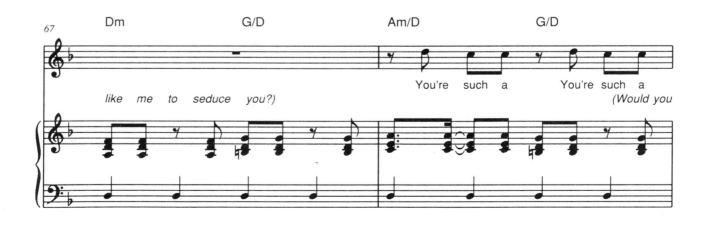

("Would you stop playing with that Radio of yours. I'm trying to get to sleep!")

TO BE WITH YOU

Words and Music by ERIC MARTIN and DAVID GRAHAME

178

TOO MUCH LOVE WILL KILL YOU

Words and Music by BRIAN MAY,
FRANK MUSKER and ELIZABETH LAMERS

184

WEATHER WITH YOU

Words and Music by NEIL FINN and TIM FINN

Moderately

189

190

Verse 2:
Well, there's a small boat made of china
It's going nowhere on the mantelpiece
Well, do I lie like a lounge room lizard
Or do I sing like a bird released?

VOGUE

Words and Music by MADONNA CICCONE and SHEP PETTIBONE

Spoken: What are you looking at?　　Vogue!　　　Strike a pose . . . . Vogue!

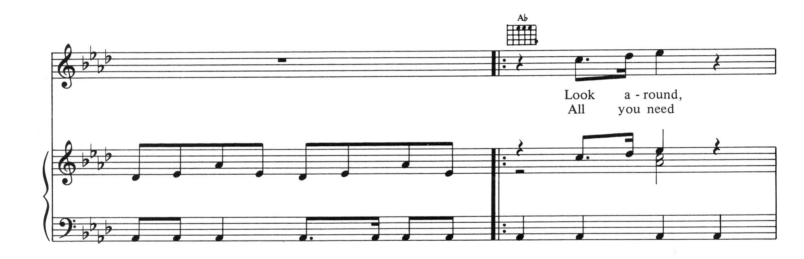

Look　a - round,
All　you need

ev - 'ry - where you turn is heart - ache,　it's ev - 'ry - where that you go. __
is your own i - ma - gi - na - tion　so use it, that's what it's for. __

D.%. al Coda   ⊕ CODA

Abno3   x4

get up on the dance floor.

(Here is where you find it!)

Vogue!

Tacet 1º

Ab   Fb   Ebm   Fb

Greta Garbo, and Monroe,
They had style, they had grace,

Dietrich and Di Maggio,
Rita Hayward gave good face

Ab   Fb   Ebm   Fb   Ab   Fb

Marlon Brando, Jimmy Dean
Lauren, Katherine, Lana too,

on the cover of a magazine.
Betty Davis, we loved you,

Grace Kelly, Harlow Jean,
ladies with an attitude

Ebm   Fb   Ab   Fb   Ebm   Fb

picture of a beauty queen.
fellas that were In The Mood.

Gene Kelly, Fred Astaire,
Don't just stand there, let's get to it, strike a pose, there's nothing to it.

Ginger Rogers, dance on air.

WOMAN TO WOMAN

Words and Music by BEVERLEY CRAVEN

Moderate, strong beat

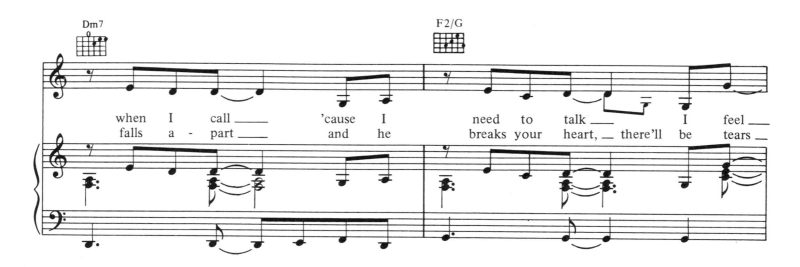

WOULD I LIE TO YOU?

Words and Music by PETER VALE and MICK LEESON

Trust _ me, ba - by.

Would I   lie   to you? Wan-na see _ you night and day.   Would I

Printed in Great Britain by Hobbs the Printers Ltd, Totton, Hampshire 3/97